Developing
Literacy
Skills

Through Science

KEY STAGE 2: Y5–6
P6–7

**FRANCES MACKAY
PENNY VERNON
LINDA CORK**

HOPSCOTCH
EDUCATIONAL PUBLISHING

/3060358

✦ Contents ✦

Published by Hopscotch Educational Publishing Ltd,
29 Waterloo Place, Leamington Spa CV32 5LA (Tel 01926 744227)

© 2000 Hopscotch Educational Publishing

Written by Frances Mackay, Penny Vernon and Linda Cork
Series design by Blade Communications
Illustrated by Virginia Gray
Cover illustration by Susan Hutchison
Printed by Clintplan, Southam

Frances Mackay, Penny Vernon and Linda Cork hereby assert their moral right to be identified as the authors of this work in accordance with the Copyright, Designs and Patents Act, 1988.

ISBN 1-902239-29-6

All rights reserved. This book is sold subject to the condition that it shall not, by way of trade or otherwise, be lent, hired out or otherwise circulated without the publisher's prior consent in any form or binding or cover other than that in which it is published and without a similar condition, including this condition, being imposed upon the subsequent purchaser.

No part of this publication may be reproduced, stored in a retrieval system, or transmitted, in any form or by any means, electronic, mechanical, photocopying, recording or otherwise, without the prior permission of the publisher, except where photocopying for educational purposes within the school or other educational establishment that has purchased this book is expressly permitted in the text.

Introduction

 **ABOUT THE SERIES**

Developing Literacy Skills Through Science is a series of books aimed at developing key literacy skills using a range of written genres based on a science theme, from Key Stage 1 (P1–3) through to Key Stage 2 (P4–7).

The series offers a structured approach which provides detailed lesson plans to teach specific literacy and science skills. A unique feature of the series is the provision of differentiated photocopiable activities aimed at considerably reducing teacher preparation time. Suggestions for follow-up activities for both literacy and science ensure maximum use of this resource.

ABOUT THIS BOOK

This book is for teachers of children at Key Stage 2, Years 5–6 and Scottish levels P6–7. It aims to:
- develop children's literacy and science skills through exposure to and experience of a wide range of stimulating texts with supporting differentiated activities which are both diversified and challenging;
- support teachers by providing practical teaching methods based on whole-class, group, paired and individual teaching;
- encourage enjoyment and curiosity as well as develop skills of interpretation and response.

 **CHAPTER CONTENT**

 Literacy objectives

These outline the aims for the literacy activities suggested in the lesson plan.

Science objectives

These outline the science learning objectives that relate to the lesson plan.

Resources

This lists the different resources that the teacher needs to teach the lesson.

Starting point: Whole class

This provides ideas for introducing the activity and may include key questions to ask the children.

Using the photocopiable text

This explains how to use the text extract provided with the children as a shared reading activity and introduction to the group work. It may also be used by groups during the group work.

Group activities

This explains how to use each sheet as well as providing guidance on the type of child who will benefit most from each sheet.

Plenary session

This suggests ideas for whole-class sessions to discuss the learning outcomes and follow-up work.

Follow-up ideas for literacy

This contains suggestions for further literacy activities related to the lesson plan which can be carried out at another time.

Follow-up ideas for science

This contains suggestions for further science activities which might be carried out at another time or during a designated science lesson.

Chapter 1

Keeping healthy

◆ Literacy objectives

◆ To read newspaper articles and headlines and consider which inform and which persuade.
◆ To consider the use of bias and how opinion can be disguised to look like fact.
◆ To write newspaper headlines.

◆ Science objectives

◆ To understand that to stay healthy we need an adequate and varied diet.

◆ Resources

◆ A collection of newspaper articles and headlines related to food, eating and other health issues, such as food poisoning, genetically-modified foods and eating disorders.

◆ Starting point: Whole class

◆ Show the children some newspaper headlines about issues such as BSE, food poisoning and salmonella. Discuss the types of words used. Are they likely to cause people to worry? Do the headlines scare people?
◆ Discuss the purpose of a headline in a newspaper. Have a couple of eye-catching headlines on other subjects available to show them. Discuss what it is that makes them effective. Do they inform us of something or are they trying to persuade us? Discuss the difference.
◆ Now read out some of the articles. Do they only contain facts? Is there an opinion anywhere in the articles? Who writes these articles? Where do they get their information from? Is everything we read in the newspaper true?
◆ Explain to the children that they are going to read parts of two articles from newspapers on genetically modified foods. Ask if anyone has heard about this. What have they heard? Have their families or friends expressed an opinion about them? Do the children have their own opinions?

◆ Using the photocopiable text

◆ Enlarge page 6 on a photocopier or ensure that each child or pair of children has a copy. Read the texts aloud as they follow or ask individuals to read them. What do the texts tell us?
◆ Consider how effective the headlines are for both pieces of text. How could they be improved? Which headline attracts them most? Why?
◆ Discuss the tone of the two texts. Which words or phrases suggest bias? Consider the first text – does it sound as if it is factual or is it biased? How can we tell? Are the children convinced more by one text than the other? Why? Which one do they believe?
◆ Consider how the two texts inform or persuade. Which words are effective in persuading and informing us?
◆ Highlight a sentence in the text. Do the children think this is fact or opinion? What other facts and opinions can they find in the texts?

◆ Group activities

Using the differentiated activity sheets

Activity sheet 1: This is aimed at those children who need most support. They are given an introductory sentence for a newspaper article and three possible headlines. They have to evaluate the headlines and choose the one they think is best and say why. They then have to write a headline for another newspaper story. They should compare their work with the rest of their group.

Activity sheet 2: This is aimed at children who are capable of writing persuasive text independently. They should identify text that is opinion and text that is factual. They have to write headlines for the two pieces of text and then write some text for a given headline. They should compare their work with the rest of their group.

Keeping healthy

Activity sheet 3: This is aimed at the more able children. It requires them to write an opening paragraph for an article that informs and another for an article that persuades, then to write a headline for a given piece of text. They should discuss their work with each other when they have finished.

◆ *Plenary session*

✦ After the children have completed their tasks, bring them together to reconsider the original text. What makes a successful headline? Can we improve on the ones we wrote at the beginning of the session? Can we begin to make a list of sentence connectives or openers that are suitable for persuading?

◆ *Follow-up ideas for literacy*

✦ Collect examples of newspaper headlines to extend the study of how effective they are.

✦ Compare two headlines from the same day dealing with the same story for differences of style and tone.

✦ Evaluate advertisements in terms of the target audience and the language used to appeal to particular consumer groups.

✦ Look at the structure of a newspaper story: headline; brief synopsis of the story; story in more detail; quotes or eye-witness accounts; follow-up/further information.

✦ Try writing a familiar story in a newspaper style, such as 'Little Red Riding Hood'.

✦ Ask the children to find out more information about genetically modified foods. Use the internet for searching. Contact organisations such as Greenpeace or Friends of the Earth to obtain an alternative point of view.

✦ Ask the children to design a poster that tells us how to eat healthily.

◆ *Follow-up ideas for science*

✦ Ask the children to tell you what they already know about healthy eating. What kinds of foods do they think they should eat in order to stay healthy? Ask them to use information sources to find out about foods that contain fats/oils, those that contain sugars/starches and those that contain essential things for growth. How much of each group do we need to eat each day? Why are fruits and vegetables so important?

✦ Collect pictures of different foods and sort them into food groups.

✦ Ask the children to keep a food diary for a week. Prepare a display of a suggested healthy diet. Ask the children to compare their diet with this one. What foods do they think they need to eat more of/less of?

✦ Ask the children to tell you what else they need to do, apart from eating a varied diet, to stay healthy. Discuss the need for daily exercise. Ask the children to tell you what they think happens to their bodies during and after exercise. Discuss how the heart pumps blood around the body to help our organs and muscles work.

✦ Show the children how to measure their pulse rate. Ask them to record their pulse rate at rest, after gentle exercise and after vigorous exercise to see what happens.

Genetically-modified foods

Food needs to be genetically modified to give extra nutrition to keep you healthy.

The Government today announced its intention to spend fifteen million pounds on a research project which will expand the use of genetically engineered foods. The food industry already makes use of a number of foods which have been altered in some way. Some crops have been made more resistant to pests thus cutting down on huge crop spraying bills. Other foods could be modified to release a larger amount of essential vitamins and minerals or to prevent the breakdown of the vitamins and minerals in cooking. A Government spokesman said, 'Genetic engineering will cut production costs and put better, healthier food on your plate.'

The food we eat may do us a lot of harm!

Today this newspaper is able to reveal the truth behind the latest Government initiative! We can reveal that huge amounts of tax payers' money are being handed to drug companies to develop foods which could poison your children! These so-called 'Frankenstein foods' have been changed so that they are no longer as nature intended. Who knows what the long-term effects will be of eating these unnatural products? We are told that the aim is to produce healthier food but we believe that the true aim is higher profits for the food growers, chemical giants and supermarkets!

✦ In the news... ✦

✦ Look at the beginning of this newspaper story and at the choice of headlines. Put a ✔ by the headline you think is the best.

Schoolboy footballers have today been warned of the dangers of over training.

'Too much exercise can be almost as bad as too little', said a spokesman for Rosebank Rovers, who currently lead Division One.

Too tired to do well!

Young talent is exhausted!

Muscle damage results from too much training!

I chose _____ as the

best headline because _____.

✦ Now write a headline for this newspaper article.

_____

_____

_____

✦ Does your headline inform people or persuade them?

_____

Parents and teachers in East Sussex were shocked to hear how many young children have died or become seriously ill this year because they chose to be slim rather than eat a proper balanced diet!

They have decided to set up a team of advisers to visit every school in the county so that children can learn how dangerous it is if they don't eat well.

◆ In the news... ◆

◆ Look at these two extracts from newspapers. One is aiming to inform the public and the other is trying to persuade the public to its point of view. Underline in red the parts that you think are fact and in blue the parts you think are opinion.

Pop stars and models are to blame for the increase in children dying from slimming diseases. This newspaper has pledged to stop this from happening. Because children want to look like their heroes and heroines we shall no longer be showing pictures of famous people who are thin! We want our children to be happy, not dead!

Recent investigations have shown that each year more and more children and teenagers die or become seriously ill because they chose to be slim rather than eat a proper balanced diet.

In West Sussex, concerned parents and teachers are to set up a team of advisers to visit each school in the county to talk to children about the dangers of not eating well.

◆ Write a headline for each extract. Make one informative and the other persuasive.

_____

_____

◆ Now look at this headline. Write some sentences that might be part of a newspaper article about this headline.

Muscle damage results from too much training!

_____

_____

_____

_____

Photocopiable

©Hopscotch Educational Publishing

◆ Look at these two newspaper headlines. Decide which is for an article that informs and which is for an article that persuades. Write an opening paragraph for each headline.

| New guidelines for schools on healthy eating | Sweets and chocolates should be banned! |

_____

_____

_____

_____

_____

_____

◆ Now look at this newspaper extract. Underline in red the words that inform and in blue the words that persuade.

◆ Write a headline for the extract.

_____

_____

_____

A recent science survey carried out by Healthtec Ltd has revealed that more and more children and teenagers are becoming seriously ill because they are choosing to diet in order to keep slim. The report states that many of the children in the survey are not eating a proper balanced diet and there are very real concerns that this will affect their health as adults. Mr Jones, a spokesperson for the company, had this to say "Parents and children need to be made aware of the importance of eating correctly. We should not be letting our children make themselves ill. Buy our food guide to help your child!"

Chapter 2

Changing sounds

◆ Literacy objectives

◆ To read and evaluate a range of instructional texts in terms of their:
  a) purposes
  b) organisation and layout
  c) clarity and usefulness
◆ To write own instructions.

◆ Science objectives

◆ To know that some materials are effective in preventing vibrations from sound sources reaching the ear.

◆ Starting point: Whole class

◆ Tell the children that a lady called Mrs Who is very unhappy because a new family has moved in next door. She is not against change but these people are very noisy and, as their houses are semi-detached, the noise travels through the walls. She tried asking them nicely to stop making so much noise but it became obvious she was having no success. So Mrs Who decided to go out and buy a soundproofing kit she had seen advertised on the television. When she got to the shop she was amazed to find that there was not one but four kits available and they were all supposed to be wonderful, according to the man in the shop. So Mrs Who decided to buy all four kits and try them.
◆ Explain to the children that each kit had a separate set of instructions. Tell them that they are going to look at three of the sets of instructions to see which they think would be most helpful for Mrs Who. They are then going to write the fourth set of instructions themselves.

◆ Using the photocopiable text

◆ Enlarge the photocopiable texts on page 12 and share them with the children. Which set of instructions do they think is most helpful? Ask them to give their reasons.
◆ Which set of instructions has the most effective layout? Would diagrams have been helpful?
◆ Ask the children how they would write instructions for each of the products to make them clearer and easier to follow. Write up some of their ideas on the board.
◆ As a class, write a set of instructions for one of the products as a model for the children to use later in the lesson.

◆ Group activities

Using the differentiated activity sheets

Activity sheet 1: This is aimed at those children who need most support. They are given the instructions but must put them in the correct order. They are also required to draw diagrams to match the instructions.

Activity sheet 2: This is aimed at children who are capable of writing simple instructions to match a diagram.

Activity sheet 3: This is aimed at more able children. It requires them to write a set of instructions for a tape. The instructions must be clear enough to understand without the aid of diagrams.

Changing sounds

◆ *Plenary session*

◆ Share the children's responses to the sheets. Do the children in Group 1 agree on the order? Can there be several correct orders? How similar are the captions/sentences in Group 2? Are they precise enough? Can others understand what they mean?

◆ How difficult did the children in Group 3 find their task? Ask someone to read out their instructions while the others sit with their eyes closed to see if they can imagine what to do if they followed these instructions. Was any important step/information left out? Why are clear, precise instructions so necessary?

◆ *Follow-up ideas for literacy*

◆ Ask the children to collect examples of lots of different types of instructions. Try to include examples of things such as how to fill in a form, how to make something and how to get to a destination. Share them to discuss their effectiveness.

◆ Ask the children to bring in the worst set of instructions they can find – perhaps one that their parents had to use to make self-assembly furniture! Challenge them to improve them!

◆ Ask the children to adapt a set of written instructions for younger children. Discuss the need for diagrams and simpler language.

◆ Compare the language of instructional text with that of informative text and notice the use of the impersonal (passive) form.

◆ Ask the children to write instructions for a 'real' purpose such as how to dismantle PE equipment correctly or how to use the computer. Make them into posters and display in the appropriate places.

◆ *Follow-up ideas for science*

◆ Carry out this experiment to investigate soundproofing:
1. Collect a variety of materials, such as carpet, paper, cotton wool, corrugated card and cork tile. Also: rice or beads.
2. Explain to the children that they are going to make a soundproofing kit for Mrs Who.
3. Make some shakers with the rice inside them.
4. Ask the children how they could devise a test to find out which material is most successful in blocking out the sound of the rice in the shakers. How will they make their test fair? When considering the results of the experiment, discuss the effect of the thickness of the materials and how this may affect the results.

◆ Ask the children to investigate noise levels in the school. Record their findings. Then discuss ways of reducing the noise in the noisiest areas.

◆ Contact a local factory to find out how noise in the workplace is combated. Ask the children to use information books and/or CD-Roms to find out the effect noise can have on our ears.

◆ Investigate the soundproofing of different walls in the school – an outer wall, inner wall, a partition etc. How can the children test this? What will they use to make a sound? How will they measure the sound level? How can they make sure the test is fair? Ask them to record their results.

Soundproofing kits

1

Wonder Web

This new Wonder product will eliminate noise with very little effort. Just a few simple steps and your house will be noise free! Just unpack Wonder Web and attach it to your wall using ordinary glue. Nothing could be easier.

2

Easy Sound

You NEED:

1. Heavy-duty wallpaper paste
2. A grease free wall surface
3. Scissors
4. Patience!!

Make sure the wall is clean and free from grease and glue from previous wallpaper. Measure each drop of *Easy Sound* and apply wallpaper paste. Put *Easy Sound* on to the wall and smooth out any air bubbles. Leave *Easy Sound* to dry for 24 hours before applying paint or wallpaper.

3

MR MAGIC SOUNDPROOFING

Instructions for use.

Remove from packaging and soak in cold water for 20 minutes.

Clean surface to which MR MAGIC is to be applied.

Measure and cut to fit to size.

Cover surface with MR MAGIC.

Leave to dry for 48 hours.

Apply paint or wallpaper.

Photocopiable

©Hopscotch Educational Publishing

◆ Soundproofing kit 4 ◆

◆ Here are the instructions for the SOUND OUT soundproofing kit. Unfortunately, the instructions are in the wrong order. Decide what the correct order should be and rewrite them. Draw some diagrams to go with the instructions.

> Soak each length of SOUND OUT in water for 2 minutes to activate the glue before hanging.
> Open the pack of SOUND OUT by tearing along the dotted line on the box.
> Cut to desired length using a sharp knife, NOT scissors.
> Remove existing wallpaper or sand down painted walls.
> Apply to a clean, dust-free wall.
> Wash wall and dry thoroughly.
> Once SOUND OUT is dry, you may decorate the wall.
> Remove inner packing and unroll SOUND OUT.

◆ Write and draw your instructions here.

Instructions for using SOUND OUT

◆ Soundproofing kit 4 ◆

◆ Here are the instructions for the SOUND OUT soundproofing kit. Unfortunately, the words are missing from each diagram. Write a short caption or sentence for each diagram so people can use the kit correctly. One has been done for you.

First, use sandpaper to sand
down the wall.

_____ _____

_____ _____

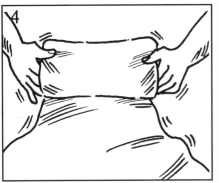

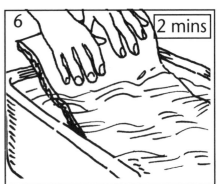

_____ _____ _____

_____ _____ _____

_____ _____

_____ _____

◆ Soundproofing kit 4 ◆

◆ Here are the diagrams for the instructions for the SOUND OUT soundproofing kit. You are going to write the instructions to go with them. The company wants to put the instructions on to tape to sell with the kit so your instructions must be clear enough for people to understand <u>without</u> the aid of diagrams!

◆ Write your instructions on another sheet of paper. <u>Remember</u>: make your instructions clear and precise.

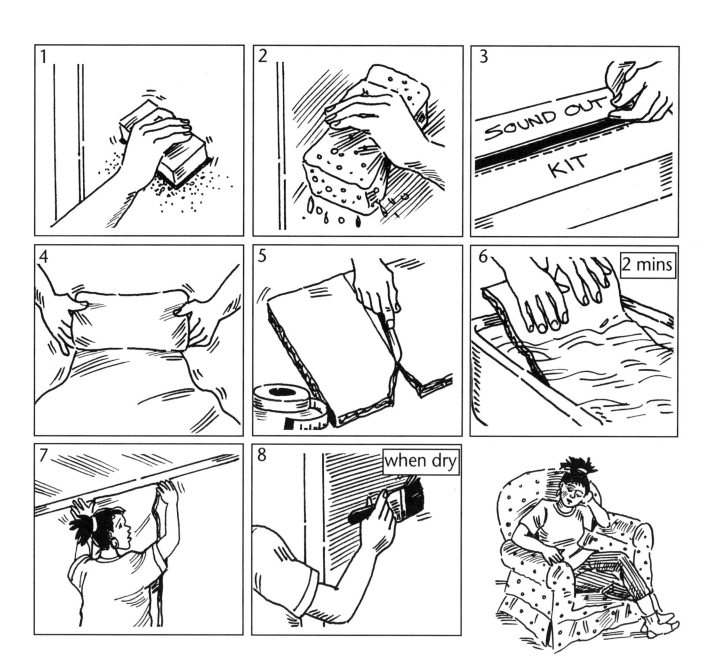

Earth, Sun and Moon

◆ Literacy objectives

◆ To read and evaluate letters that inform and persuade, considering how they are set out and how the language is used.
◆ To write a commentary on an issue, setting out and justifying a personal view.

◆ Science objectives

◆ To understand that the Earth is approximately spherical.
◆ To understand that evidence may be interpreted in more than one way.

◆ Resources

◆ Some pictures showing Earth from space and some books on space travel.

◆ Starting point: Whole class

◆ Tell the children that they are going to read some letters written long ago to a king asking him for money to help prove whether the Earth was round or flat. Ask the children what they think – is it spherical or flat? How do they know this? Briefly discuss how at one time many people believed the Earth to be flat because that was how it looked. They believed that the horizon was the edge of the Earth because they couldn't see anything beyond it. Explain that the scientists of that time couldn't agree – both sides thinking that they were right. Discuss how scientific ideas can change over time (through new discoveries and inventions) and how earlier people's ideas may seem ridiculous to us now but that at the time their ideas were based on the evidence available to them. Will the ideas we have today change in the future?
◆ What do the children think may have happened to prove that the world is round? (Sailors eventually sailed all the way round; space exploration.) Show them pictures of Earth from space.

◆ Using the photocopiable text

◆ Enlarge the texts on page 18 on a photocopier or arrange for each pair of children to have a copy. Share the texts, reminding them that these letters were written long ago.
◆ What is the purpose of the two letters? In what ways are they similar/different? What personal points of view are being expressed by each person? How effective are they in putting across these views?
◆ Look at the way the letters are set out. Are they personal letters such as they might write to a friend or business-type letters? What tells them this? Note the use of the first person.
◆ Look at the language used. What words and phrases does each person use to try and persuade the king to fund their ideas? Underline them in the texts. Do the letter writers try to flatter the king? Why do they think they might do this? Do they provide him with any evidence or facts? Do the children consider the letters to be well written? Do they serve their purpose or could they be improved? How would the children respond to each letter if they were the king? Why?
◆ Explain that today, too, governments have to decide how to spend their money. Tell the children that they are now going to have the opportunity to express their own point of view about whether or not governments should spend money on space exploration. (If appropriate, briefly share the books about space exploration to help the children understand some of the projects that have taken place, such as probes to Mars and space stations.)

◆ Group activities

Using the differentiated activity sheets

Activity sheet 1: This is aimed at children who need more support in developing a point of view. They are given lists of reasons for and against space exploration to help them decide their own view about the issue.

Earth, Sun and Moon

Activity sheet 2: This is aimed at children who are able to add their own points of view on an issue. They are required to write a list of persuasive reasons for or against space exploration.

Activity sheet 3: This is aimed at more able children. They are required to write their own lists of reasons for and against space exploration and then explain their own point of view, using persuasive reasons.

◆ *Plenary session*

✦ Share the responses to the activity sheets. Ask someone in Group 3 to read out their reasons. How persuasive are they? What words/phrases were used that might persuade someone that their point of view is right? How difficult is it to justify your own point of view?

◆ *Follow-up ideas for literacy*

✦ Ask the children to write a letter to the king (or queen) as on page 18, asking him (or her) to support their request for money to either continue space exploration or use for some other specified purpose.
✦ Write letters in different styles – to inform, to protest or to complain. Look at examples in newspapers.
✦ Carry out a class debate – for and against space exploration.

✦ Ask the children to find more information about space exploration using information books, CD-Roms and the Internet. Does this alter their views about its usefulness and purpose?
✦ Design advertising posters/leaflets that inform and persuade others. Look at advertisements in magazines to discuss the language used to gain attention and persuade people.

◆ *Follow-up ideas for science*

✦ Ask the children to find information about people's earlier ideas about whether the Earth was round or flat. What evidence did people use to support their theories?
✦ Find out about Galileo and his theories about the Sun's place in the solar system.
✦ Explore the forces of gravity. Ask the children to investigate whether objects of the same shape but different weights fall to the ground at the same speed. Ask the children to make Plasticene balls of different weights. Drop them from the same height. Which one will reach the ground first? Why? Does changing the shape affect the result?

✦ Challenge the children to make their own rocket! Look at pictures of rockets. Discuss what shapes they are and why. Look at the launch pads – why do they need to be so strong? Talk about how a model could be made and the possible methods of propulsion, such as balloons, springs or rubber bands. (Discuss safety issues and closely supervise all launchings.)

Letters to the king

KS2 Y5-6/P6-7

Your Majesty,

As a loyal subject of your gracious Majesty, I write to offer you the results of my research and hope to gain your Majesty's approval and support for my continuing work.

For some years now, as your Majesty is aware, I have been engaged in an investigation of the extent of the Earth's surface, and have come to a conclusion based on scientific research. I am proud to inform your Majesty that this world extends for some five days sailing in all directions from a central point (that being the port of London). In addition I have confirmed, not without the loss of some brave hands, that the sea is cold nearer the northern edges of the world but warmer nearer its southern boundary.

I now wish to continue my research by investigating the method which is employed to keep the water on our Earth, since, as your Majesty will be aware, water cannot be contained on a flat surface without flowing away. My theory is that at the very outermost edge, a wall or boundary will be discovered which prevents the escape of our seas into the abyss below. Such an important wall, when discovered, would require a memorable name and, with your permission, Sire, I had considered the use of 'The Great King George's Barrier'.

I shall eagerly await news of your Majesty's support.

> *Your loyal subject,*
> *Nathaniel Thackery*

Your Majesty,

After many hours of arduous study and much calculation, I, Frederick Baker, have made such a discovery that I felt your Majesty needed to be informed directly!

Using my own mathematical formula, I have calculated that the Earth must be round. My calculations, so far, suggest that the surface of the Earth must be curved in shape. Using my most powerful telescope (a new invention for looking at the stars) I have noted that even on the clearest of days it is impossible to see further than a curved surface would allow.

With the financial support of your Majesty, I propose to build a very high tower to allow my theories to be tested further. For, if the world is round, then my calculations will yield the same result from the top of the tower as they do from the ground, namely that the horizon is 27 miles away and that therefore the Earth must be curved.

> Your obedient servant,
> Rev. Frederick Baker

Photocopiable
©Hopscotch Educational Publishing

Space exploration

◆ Here are two points of view about space exploration. Read them through carefully.

<table>
<tr><td>

Reasons FOR space exploration

1. It has helped us to learn things about the Moon and planets that we did not know about before.
2. It has enabled us to put up satellites that have greatly improved telephone and TV communications.
3. Studies of astronauts have helped many developments in medicine.
4. As the world population increases, we may need to find other planets on which to live.
5. Modern space rockets such as the space shuttle are reusable – this saves money.

</td><td>

Reasons AGAINST space exploration

1. It costs far too much money. Governments should be spending money on other things.
2. There are already too many satellites orbiting the Earth – they might fall and kill people.
3. We might meet aliens who are not friendly. They might come and attack us.
4. People have died in space accidents.
5. We need to solve problems here on Earth rather than worry about other planets.

</td></tr>
</table>

◆ What do YOU think about space exploration? Should governments spend money on it? Complete the following to give your own personal view.

I think governments _____ spend money on space exploration. I think this because: (List your reasons.)

1

2

3

◆ Share your views with someone else. Do they agree or disagree?

✦ Space exploration ✦

✦ Here are some reasons for and against space exploration. Add two more reasons of your own for each box.

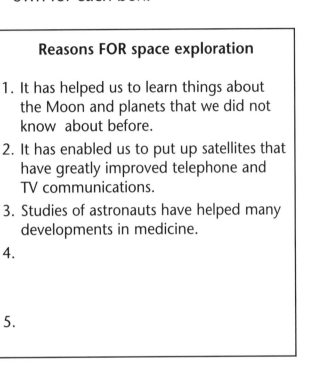

Reasons FOR space exploration	Reasons AGAINST space exploration
1. It has helped us to learn things about the Moon and planets that we did not know about before. 2. It has enabled us to put up satellites that have greatly improved telephone and TV communications. 3. Studies of astronauts have helped many developments in medicine. 4. 5.	1. It costs far too much money. Governments should be spending money on other things. 2. There are already too many satellites orbiting the Earth – they might fall and kill people. 3. We might meet aliens who are not friendly. They might come and attack us. 4. 5.

✦ Imagine you have to write to the Government to persuade them to either continue spending money on space exploration or stop it altogether. List the reasons **you** would give below. Use suitable language to persuade them that you are right.

Photocopiable

©Hopscotch Educational Publishing

✦ Space exploration ✦

✦ List some reasons FOR and AGAINST space travel.
Use information books to help you.

Reasons FOR space exploration	Reasons AGAINST space exploration

✦ Now decide which of these points of view you agree with – FOR or AGAINST.
Write down WHY you think this, giving persuasive reasons for your point of view.

Life-cycles – plants

◆ Literacy objectives

◆ To use dictionaries efficiently to explore spellings and meanings.
◆ To write own definitions of words.
◆ To search for and define technical words to make a glossary.

◆ Science objectives

◆ To know that flowering plants reproduce.
◆ To know that insects pollinate some flowers.
◆ To know that plants that produce flowers have male and female organs and that seeds are formed when pollen from the male organ fertilises the female organ.

◆ Resources

◆ Some information books about flowering plants that contain a glossary.
◆ Dictionaries.

◆ Starting point: Whole class

◆ Tell the children that they are going to be doing some work on flowering plants. Show them the collection of books. Explain that if they wanted to find information about flower parts and how they work, they could use books such as these. Where might they look first to find out about petals, for example? Discuss the use of the contents and index pages.
◆ Turn to a page that shows an illustration of the parts of the flowering plant and their names. Briefly share the names of the different parts explaining that they will be finding out more about them during the lesson. Point out a technical word such as stigma. Remind them that some books have a glossary. Why might this be necessary? Where could they find out the meaning of a technical word if the book did not contain a glosssary?
◆ Look up some of the definitions in the glossaries of several of the books. Consider the language

that is used. Are they written in full sentences or are they contracted? Model how sentences can be contracted and retain their meaning.

◆ Using the photocopiable text

◆ Enlarge the text on page 24 on a photocopier or arrange for each pair of children to have a copy. Share the text with the children, either reading it out loud yourself or asking different children to read different parts of the text.
◆ Discuss the style in which the passage is written. How would it be described (genre)? What words or phrases typify this style? How effective is it in helping us to remember the main stages in the process of plant fertilisation?
◆ Reread the text, asking the children to tell you which words they think should be included in a glossary. Underline them. Agree the words. Then consider the following: is it possible to work out the meaning of an unfamiliar word from the context? If not, are these the words that need to go in a glossary? Discuss the fact that although the children themselves may know the meaning of some of these words, other people may not, so it is important to include all the words they think will be helpful in order to understand the passage.
◆ How can we find out if the selected words have been spelled correctly? Revise how to find words in a dictionary using the guide words.
◆ Practise writing definitions by asking the children to think of their own definitions for the words 'tree' and 'leaf'. Share the responses and check with different dictionaries and glossaries to compare definitions.

◆ Group activities

Using the differentiated activity sheets

Activity sheet 1: This is aimed at children who need support in writing their own definitions. They are required to write definitions of words that are already defined in the text.

Life-cycles – plants

Activity sheet 2: This is aimed at children who are more confident in using a dictionary and writing their own definitions.

Activity sheet 3: This is aimed at more able children. They are required to identify spelling errors and technical words in a passage and to write a definition of these words.

◆ *Plenary session*

◆ Share the responses to the activity sheets. Do they agree on the definitions? How difficult is it to write a definition? What advice could they give to others? How do their own definitions compare with a dictionary or glossary? How important is it to be clear and precise?

◆ *Follow-up ideas for literacy*

◆ Ask the children to try and write in the same style as the shared text on a different topic. Does this way of writing help others to remember the facts contained in the text?

◆ Ask the children to write an information sheet for younger children about flowering plant parts. How will they need to change the text to suit the audience? Which technical words will be included? Which ones omitted? Why?

◆ Explore words which have more than one meaning or a meaning in science and an everyday meaning, for example: cell, stalk.

◆ Look for little words in longer technical words such as: photosynthesis – photos, hot, to, the, he, is, sis.

◆ Challenge the children to use CD-Roms and/or information books to find out more about flowering plants.

◆ Encourage the children to become familiar with a wide range of dictionaries such as dictionaries of slang or idioms and thesauruses.

◆ *Follow-up ideas for science*

◆ Look at diagrams or models of flowering plant parts and compare them with real flowers. Provide the children with a sample of flowers which have a large base or receptacle. Encourage them to look for differences and similarities in the shape, colour, smell, texture, number of petals, number of flowers on each stem and so on. Ask them to do observational drawings of them. Then cut up the flowers to look at the flower parts. Use hand lenses or a microscope for more detailed observation.

◆ Leave some cut flowers in water in the classroom. Observe what happens. Why don't they produce seeds?

◆ Plant cress seeds on damp blotting paper and ask the children to make observational diaries of what happens.

◆ Collect a wide variety of seeds. Ask the children to observe them closely to find the features they have which are adapted for dispersal (such as the parachute of the dandelion, hooks of the burdock and wings of the sycamore and ash).

◆ Propagate some plants in different ways: grow some plants from seeds by following the instructions on the packets; remove a plantlet from spider plants and place in a jar of water; take a stem cutting from a busy lizzie and place it in watered compost, or remove a whole leaf from a succulent and push the end into watered compost.

The adventures of Len Grain

Let me introduce myself. The name's Len Grain and I want to tell you about the exciting adventure I had the other day. Anyway, there I was, minding my own business and admiring the beautifully coloured petals surrounding me when Buzzzzzzzzzzzzzzzzzzzzzzzzzzzzzzz – there came this huge noise and the sky got darker. Well, before you could say pollen grain, I was carried away from all my brothers and from the stamen which had always been my home.

I was carried along high above the garden by this great bumbling creature and then suddenly it decided to land on one of the neighbouring flowers. I was thrown off without a word of apology from the great buzzing monster and there I was all alone sitting on what I can only assume was a stigma.

Anyway, as I said, there I was stuck with nowhere else to go and no way off. So what did I do? I dug down! That's what I did! I burrowed my way downwards through the style and found myself in a kind of cave which I now know was an ovary. I began talking to the locals (they're called ovules, by the way) and they said that there's only one way out and it's going to take some time! They said my only chance is to join forces with one of them and become a seed. Of course, life won't be quite the same, but once the seed is mature I am told that it will be dispersed and then I will find myself back in the outside world! Then there's a chance that I will germinate and grow into a whole new plant!

What do you make of that then?

Photocopiable
©Hopscotch Educational Publishing

◆ Definitions ◆

◆ Read the following passage from an
   information book about flowering plants.

> Every part of a flowering plant has a special purpose. The <u>roots</u> anchor the
> plant in the ground. They also take up water and <u>nutrients</u> from the soil. The
> <u>stem</u> supports the leaves, flowers and fruit. It also carries water from the roots
> to the leaves and carries food made in the leaves to other parts of the plant.
> The <u>leaves</u> are flat blades attached to the stem. They are usually green. They
> make food for the plant. The <u>flowers</u> contain the <u>reproductive organs</u> and
> most flowers have both male and female parts.

◆ Look at the underlined words. These words are found in a glossary
   at the back of the book. Write them out here in dictionary order.

◆ Write your own definitions of the following words for the glossary.

roots_____

_____

leaves_____

_____

◆ Now use a dictionary or glossary and write out the definitions
   to compare them with yours.

roots_____

_____

leaves_____

_____

✦ Definitions ✦

✦ Read the following passage from an
information book about flowering plants.

> Every part of a flowering plant has a special purpose. The <u>roots</u> anchor the
> plant in the ground as well as taking up water and <u>nutriants</u> from the soil. The
> <u>stem</u> supports the leaves, flowers and fruit. It also carries water from the roots
> to the leaves and carries food made in the leaves to other parts of the plant.
> The <u>leaves</u> make food for the plant through a process called <u>photosinthesis</u>.
> The <u>flowers</u> contain the <u>reproductive organs</u> and most flowers have both male
> and female parts. The female part (the <u>pistil</u>) consists of the <u>stigma</u>, <u>style</u>,
> <u>ovary</u> and <u>ovules</u> (eggs). The male part (the <u>stamen</u>) consists of the <u>anther</u> and
> <u>filament</u>.

✦ Look at the words underlined. These words are found in a glossary at the
back of the book. Unfortunately, two of the words are spelled incorrectly.
Circle the words you think are incorrect and use a dictionary to write the
correct spellings here.

_____   _____

✦ Write your own definitions of the following words for the glossary.

stem_____

_____

flowers_____

_____

ovules _____

_____

stamen _____

_____

✦ Now use a dictionary to compare your definitions with the dictionary ones.

Photocopiable

©Hopscotch Educational Publishing

◆ Definitions ◆

◆ Below is a passage from an information book about flowering plants. Unfortunately, four of the words are spelled incorrectly. Circle the words you think are incorrect and use a dictionary to write in the correct spellings.

Every part of a flowering plant has a special purpose. The roots anchor the plant in the ground as well as taking up water and nutriants from the soil. The stem supports the leaves, flowers and fruit. It also carries water from the roots to the leaves and carries food made in the leaves to other parts of the plant. The leaves make food for the plant through a process called photosinthesis. The flowers contain the reproductive organs and most flowers have both male and female parts. The female part (the pistol) consists of the stigma, style, ovary and ovules (eggs). The male part (the staman) consists of the anther and filament.

◆ Write the correct spellings here.

_____

_____

_____

_____

◆ Now underline all the words you think should go in a glossary at the back of the book. List them here and write your own definition for each word.

◆ Finally, use a dictionary to compare your definitions with the dictionary ones.

Life cycles – animals

◆ Literacy objectives

◆ To adapt writing for different audiences and purposes by changing the vocabulary, tone and sentence structure.
◆ To plan, compose, edit or refine short non-chronological reports or explanatory texts focusing on clarity, conciseness and impersonal style.

◆ Science objectives

◆ To know that animals have young and that these grow into adults which in turn produce young.

◆ Resources

◆ A collection of information books written for primary children of different ages.

◆ Starting point: Whole class

◆ Tell the children that they are going to be looking at a collection of information books that have been written for children of different ages. Show some pages from a book written for 10- to 11-year-olds and then compare it with some pages from a book written for four- to five-year-olds. Ask the children to tell you all the differences in language and layout they notice. For example: Is the text size different? Does the amount of text/ pictures on the page vary? Is there a difference in the technical language used?
◆ Explain that they are going to consider this in more detail now by looking at two extracts from some books on animal life cycles.

◆ Using the photocopiable text

◆ Enlarge the text on page 30 on a photocopier or arrange for each pair of children to have a copy. (Cut the page in half so the text and cyclical diagram are separate) Give the children the text section first. Share it with them, either reading it out loud yourself or asking different children to read different parts of the text.
◆ What information does it give us? Would this text be suitable for younger children? If not, why not? Discuss the vocabulary in the text and its suitability for a younger audience.
◆ Next, share the cyclical diagram. How might this be more suitable for younger children? Discuss why it is called a cyclical diagram. Do pictures help younger children understand the text? Would a child unable to read still get information from this diagram?
◆ Evaluate the vocabulary used on the diagram for use with younger children. Have less technical words been used? Is the sentence structure simpler?
◆ Explain that they will now be writing some information for younger children in a similar way to the shared example.

◆ Group activities

Using the differentiated activity sheets

Activity sheet 1: This is aimed at children who need a simpler text from which to obtain information in order to label a cyclical diagram.

Activity sheet 2: This is aimed at children who require a more challenging text but who need support with setting out and labelling the cyclical diagram.

Activity sheet 3: This is aimed at more able children who are confident enough to edit a text to construct their own cyclical diagram.

Life cycles – animals

✦ *Plenary session*

✦ Share the responses to the activity sheets. Have the stages been summarised using the appropriate vocabulary, tone and sentence structure for a younger audience? What problems did they have? What decisions did they have to make? Has Group 3 chosen the same things to write and illustrate as Groups 1 and 2? How useful do they think cyclical diagrams are?

✦ *Follow up ideas for literacy*

✦ Consider adaptations to text other than the one used for younger readers, for example: how does vocabulary, tone and sentence structure need to be adapted when writing a prayer or a match report?

✦ Ask the children to write an information book about the life cycle of the butterfly or frog. Encourage them to find out more information by using CD-Roms, books and the internet.

✦ Ask the children to make a glossary of technical words used in the frog and butterfly text, for example 'metamorphosis' and 'frogspawn'.

✦ Dramatise the stages in development of the butterfly or frog. The children could write the narration for a mimed sequence or they could write a short play about the amazing changes that take place.

✦ Challenge the children to write about the life cycles of other animals in cyclical diagrams.

✦ *Follow up ideas for science*

✦ Challenge the children to use secondary sources to find out what other insect groups metamorphose as part of their life cycle. Do they do it in the same way as Lepidoptera?

✦ Consider the habitats that frogs and toads live in. Does this have a connection with their life cycle? Do frogs and toads need water? In what ways are frogs and toads adapted to their habitat?

✦ Go out into the local area. Study two different habitats. What are the similarities and differences between the animals that live there? How do the conditions in the habitats differ?

✦ Discuss why it is so important that animals are able to reproduce. Ask the children to find out about animals that have become extinct. What are the reasons for their extinction? What animals are endangered today? Why? What can be done about this?

✦ Compare the life cycles of humans with other animals. How do the stages compare? How long is the gestation period or how long do the young stay with their parents, for example? Use a time line to demonstrate the differences and similarities.

✦ Compare the life cycles of animals with flowering plants. In what ways are they similar? In what ways are they different?

The life cycle of the butterfly

Butterflies and moths together make up an insect group called Lepidoptera, a name which means 'scaly winged' and in which there are over 120 000 species. Lepidoptera have an unusual life cycle. The adults lay the eggs on a suitable plant food for the young to eat. So, when the eggs hatch and the caterpillar emerges, it can begin eating straight away, using its powerful jaws.

As the caterpillar grows, its outer skin is shed and replaced to allow further growth. When the caterpillar reaches its full size it attaches itself to a suitable location by silken threads and undergoes metamorphosis to change itself into the adult form. The caterpillar achieves metamorphosis by turning itself into a pupa or chrysalis. When metamorphosis is complete, the adult emerges. At first its wings are damp and crumpled but the butterfly expands them by forcing blood into the veins. The adult then finds a mate, reproduces and the cycle begins again.

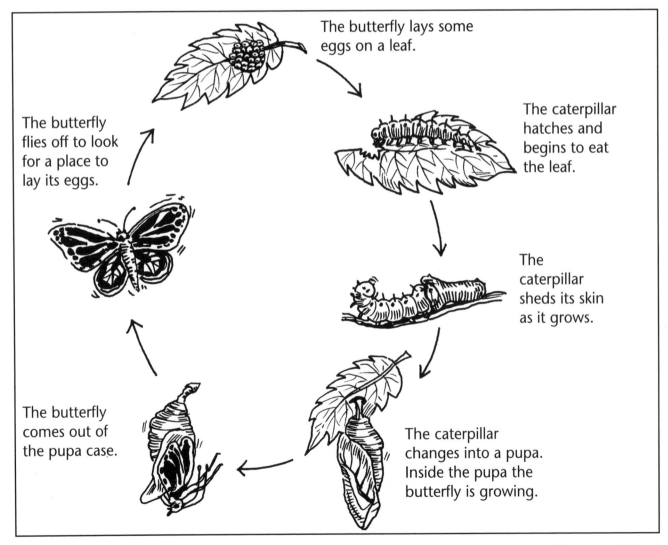

The butterfly lays some eggs on a leaf.

The caterpillar hatches and begins to eat the leaf.

The caterpillar sheds its skin as it grows.

The caterpillar changes into a pupa. Inside the pupa the butterfly is growing.

The butterfly comes out of the pupa case.

The butterfly flies off to look for a place to lay its eggs.

Photocopiable

©Hopscotch Educational Publishing

◆ Life cycle of the frog ◆

◆ Read the text below. You are going to use the information in it to label a diagram. The diagram is for children who are younger than you so make sure your labels are written at a suitable level.

In spring, frogs come to ponds to lay their eggs. Frogs eggs are called frogspawn. The frogspawn looks like a mass of jelly with lots of black dots inside it. Each black dot is actually an egg. The eggs grow and change shape and, after a while, a tiny tadpole comes out and fastens itself to the jelly. The tadpole eats the jelly and then swims away to find safety in some pond weed.

   The tadpole grows bigger and stronger. Soon it starts to eat insects as well as pond weed. At about four weeks, the tadpole grows back legs and in another three or four weeks the front legs start to grow. Finally, the tail begins to get shorter and shorter and the tadpole turns into a frog.

   The frog then leaves the pond and, when it is fully grown, returns to lay its eggs and the cycle begins again.

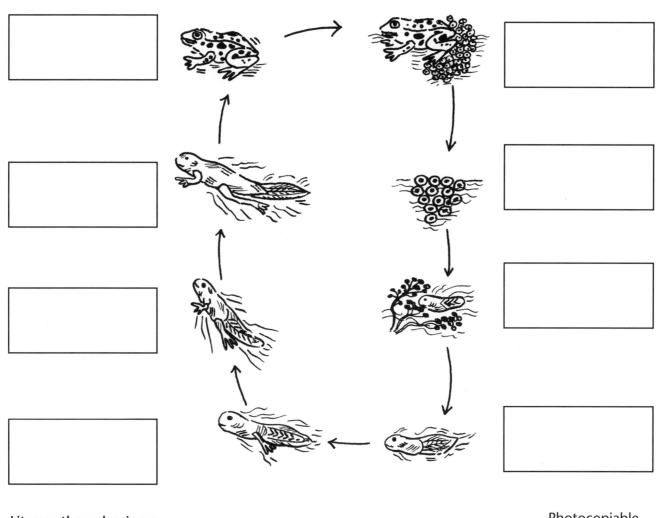

✦ Life cycle of the frog ✦

✦ Read the text below. You are going to use the information
in it to label the cyclical diagram at the bottom of the
page. The diagram is for children who are younger than
you so make sure your labels are written at a suitable level.

Frogs are amphibians – animals capable of living on water and on land. The frog lays its
eggs in water because they are prone to desiccation. The egg is surrounded by a
nutritious jelly-like substance which provides the developing embryo with the necessary
energy for growth.

The eggs hatch into swimming, fish-like creatures called tadpoles which have external
gills and suckers to attach themselves to their food source. After about four weeks, the
external gills are replaced by internal ones and the tadpole begins to swim freely. The
tadpoles eat pond weed and insects and begin to grow in size. Gradually each tadpole
undergoes a complete change or metamorphosis. First it develops back legs, then front
legs and finally its tail shortens until the tiny frog is ready to emerge from the water. The
whole process takes about three months.

When mature, the frog returns to the pond to lay its eggs and the whole process
begins again.

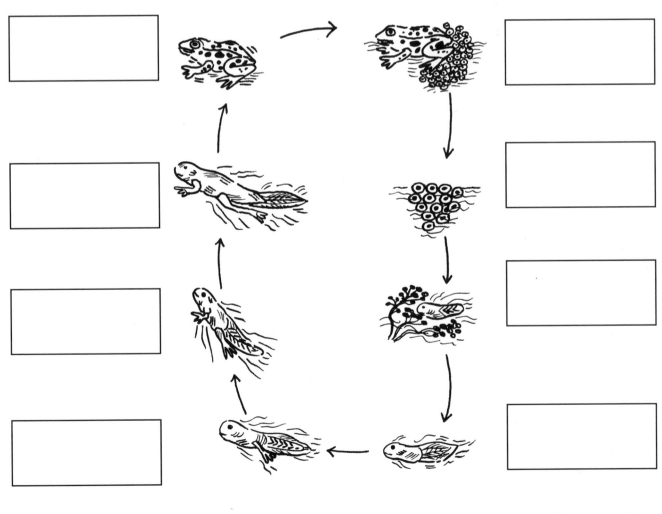

Photocopiable
©Hopscotch Educational Publishing

✦ Life cycle of the frog ✦

✦ Read the text below. You are going to use the information in it to draw and label a cyclical diagram for younger children. Make sure your labels are written at a suitable level.

Frogs are amphibians – animals capable of living on water and on land. The frog lays its eggs in water because they are prone to desiccation. The egg is surrounded by a nutritious jelly-like substance which provides the developing embryo with the necessary energy for growth.

The eggs hatch into swimming, fish-like creatures called tadpoles which have external gills and suckers to attach themselves to their food source. After about four weeks, the external gills are replaced by internal ones and the tadpole begins to swim freely. The tadpoles eat pond weed and insects and begin to grow in size. Gradually each tadpole undergoes a complete change or metamorphosis. First it develops back legs, then front legs and finally its tail shortens until the tiny frog is ready to emerge from the water. The whole process takes about three months.

When mature, the frog returns to the pond to lay its eggs and the whole process begins again.

Micro-organisms

◆ Literacy objectives

◆ To explore the use of conditionals, such as 'if... then', 'might', 'could', 'would', and their uses, such as in deduction, speculation and supposition.
◆ To use conditionals to construct sentences which express speculation or hypotheses.

◆ Science objectives

◆ To know that there are very small organisms called micro-organisms which can be harmful.
◆ To know that micro-organisms can cause food to decay.
◆ To know that food needs to be handled and stored with care.

◆ Resources

◆ Some pictures of micro-organisms such as bacteria.

◆ Starting point: Whole class

◆ Tell the children that they are going to read some information about the work of a scientist called Louis Pasteur (1822–1895). Explain that he carried out his work a long time ago when people were unaware of how common diseases were caused and how to prevent them from happening.
◆ Explain that he was one of the first scientists to discover the microscopic organisms called micro-organisms or microbes (germs). If possible, show them a picture of some bacteria and remind them that they are actually too small to be seen with the naked eye.
◆ Talk to the children about the fact that much of the scientific knowledge we take for granted today was once only theory and that some of these theories seemed almost ridiculous in the past. Discuss how some of the knowledge that we hold today might be considered to be quaint and old-fashioned in the future.

◆ Using the photocopiable text

◆ Enlarge the text on page 36 on a photocopier or arrange for each pair of children to have a copy. Share the text.
◆ What does the text tell us about how people thought diseases were caused at that time? Explain that such ideas could be termed supposition (to presume something is true without certain knowledge) or speculation (to conjecture without knowing all the facts). Point out the conditionals in the text, such as 'could' and 'might' that support these. Look at other conditionals used such as 'if... then'.
◆ Discuss other examples of speculation and supposition from everyday life to ensure the children understand the meaning of the terms. For example, 'The hole in the skirting-board might be caused by mice.'
◆ Compare these terms with deduction (a conclusion worked out by a process of reasoning). Find an example of deduction in the text.
◆ Model constructing sentences that use conditionals to express possibilities or hypotheses. For example, 'If the weather remains fine, then we can go swimming' or 'If the paper turns red, then sugar is present.'

◆ Group activities

Using the differentiated activity sheets

Activity sheet 1: This is aimed at children who need support in completing sentences with the conditionals missing.

Activity sheet 2: This is aimed at children who are able to select the missing conditionals without guidance in the text.

Activity sheet 3: This is aimed at more able children. It requires them to recognise deductions, speculations and suppositions as well as completing a passage with the conditionals missing.

Micro-organisms

◆ *Plenary session*

◆ Share the responses to the activity sheets. Can they justify their choice of words? Do others agree on the selections of conditionals? Can there be more than one suitable answer? Share the examples of deduction, speculation and supposition from Activity sheet 3 to revise the meanings of these terms.

◆ *Follow-up ideas for literacy*

◆ Consider how the use of conditionals in the past and future tenses leads to a change in the vocabulary used, for example: 'Because... then... happened.' or 'If... then... will/might happen.'

◆ Ask the children to find more information about Pasteur and van Leeuenhoek using information books, CD-Roms and the Internet.

◆ Ask the children to imagine they are Pasteur or his assistant. They could retell the information in a diary, scientific report or first person account.

◆ Read biographies and autobiographies about other scientists. Discuss the differences between the two. Ask the children to write in a biographical style about one of the scientists.

◆ Write newspaper reports about the discoveries of Pasteur and van Leeuenhoek. Look at copies of newspapers of the time to discuss an appropriate writing style. Compare with the newspaper style of today.

◆ *Follow-up ideas for science*

◆ Discuss how micro-organisms bring about decay. Why is this important? How is it beneficial to the environment? What would happen if things did not decay?

◆ Ask the children to use information books/the Internet to find more information about the role of micro-organisms in food production, for example in the making of yoghurt.

◆ Over several weeks, observe some foods, such as bread, cheese or fruit, in sealed containers. Ask the children to keep a diary of what happens to the food. What causes mould? How can it affect us if we eat it?

◆ Conduct an experiment to find out whether the temperature at which yeast culture is grown affects its speed of reproduction. Collect several beakers, dried yeast and sugar. Prepare the yeast as suggested on the packet. Put the yeast in the beakers and cover the tops with plastic bags and secure them with an elastic band. Place them in different places, such as the fridge, the classroom, on top of a heater and so on. Watch to see how quickly the bags fill with carbon dioxide. Can the children suggest how they might ensure their results are correct? What other factors can they think of that might affect the rate of growth of the yeast.

Louis Pasteur

Louis Pasteur was a scientist who spent many years studying tiny living creatures, too small to be seen with the naked eye, called micro-organisms. His discoveries changed the way people thought about disease and hygiene.

For centuries people had tried to explain what caused diseases. Some people said that diseases could be a punishment from God because the sick person had been sinful. Others believed that evil spirits or demons might have invaded the

sufferer and caused the disease. A very common belief was that bad, smelly air was the cause, so in the Middle Ages, people carried nosegays of flowers, herbs or spices in the belief that their strong smell would keep away infections.

Pasteur was inclined to believe that micro-organisms could cause disease. This idea had been put forward before but there was no convincing evidence to support it. As it happened, the evidence Pasteur wanted actually came to him by accident. He had been working on vaccinations, injecting micro-organisms found in diseased chickens into healthy ones to prove that the micro-organisms caused the disease. An assistant was in charge of doing the injections. One day, just before he was going on holiday, the assistant forgot to inject the chickens and the bacteria were left for several weeks in a cupboard. When he got back, he realised what he had done and quickly injected some healthy chickens. Instead of becoming very ill and dying, they only became slightly ill and then recovered. The assistant did not understand why this should be so he went to Pasteur and confessed what had happened.

Pasteur told him to make some more new deadly vaccine quickly and inject it into the recovered chickens. They did not fall ill at all. To make absolutely sure the vaccine *was* deadly, Pasteur bought some new chickens and injected them. If they died then he knew he was on to a new discovery. They did die and from this experiment Pasteur worked out that something happens to a vaccine

that is left for several weeks that causes it to change to something that actually protects against disease. He then began to carry out further experiments to find out if these 'protective micro-organisms' could help fight disease in humans as well as chickens.

◆ Food safety ◆

◆ Read the text below carefully. It tells you all about food safety.

Most foods have bacteria in them. Some kinds of bacteria can be good for us and <u>some can make us ill</u>. We therefore <u>need to kill or reduce the harmful bacteria </u>in food before we eat it. This can be done in several ways.

1. <u>Heat the food</u> to a very high temperature. Milk and canned foods can be treated in this way.
2. Remove the water from the food (dried foods). Bacteria cannot live without water. <u>Once water is added to dried food the bacteria grow again.</u>
3. <u>Remove the air</u> inside food packages (vacuum-packed foods).
4. <u>Put food in a fridge or freezer.</u> The <u>growth of bacteria slows down in cold conditions.</u>

◆ Now complete the sentences below. Choose words from the box and the underlined sentences to help you.

if… then	could	would	might	until
because	when	if	so	

1. We need to kill off harmful bacteria in foods _____ they can make us ill.

2. _____ food is heated to a high temperature, bacteria are killed.

3. ____ water is added to dried foods _____ bacteria can grow again.

4. Fresh food should be kept in a fridge _____ it is ready to be eaten.

5. _____ the air is removed from food packages, the bacteria die.

6. _____ food is kept in cold conditions the growth of bacteria is slowed down.

✦ Food safety ✦

✦ Read the text below. It contains information about food safety.

Most packaged foods today have a label that tells us the sell-by date and the use-by date. These dates are put there to protect us by making sure the food is still fresh when it is eaten.

All foods contain bacteria, some of which can be harmful to us and some of which can be good for us. The harmful bacteria need to be killed or reduced before we eat the food or we can get food poisoning. Milk and many canned foods are heated to a very high temperature before being sold. This kills the bacteria. If this wasn't done, people could become very ill. Another way to keep food safe is to dry it. Bacteria cannot live without water so dried foods are safe to eat, but if moisture is added then the bacteria begin to grow again.

When food is put into a fridge or freezer, the bacteria do not die but their growth rapidly slows down. Once the food is taken out of the cold and gets warm again, the bacteria grow quickly. This is why thawed foods should be cooked and eaten straight away. Bacteria can also be killed by removing the air inside a package. This is why vacuum-packed foods can last for a very long time. But once the seal is broken and air gets in the bacteria grow again.

✦ Now complete the sentences below. Choose words from the box to help you.

if...then	could	would	might	until
because	when		if	so

1. We need to kill off harmful bacteria in foods _____ they can make us ill.

2. _____ food is heated to a high temperature, bacteria are killed.

3. ____ water is added to dried foods _____ bacteria can grow again.

4. Fresh food should be kept in a fridge _____ it is ready to be eaten.

5. _____ the air is removed from food packages, the bacteria die.

6. _____ food is kept in cold conditions the growth of bacteria is slowed down.

◆ Food safety ◆

◆ Read the text below. It contains
   information about food safety.

In 1677, a man called Anton van Leeuenhoek built a microscope and used it to look
at a drop of water. He saw that it contained lots of tiny rod-shaped creatures. After
many observations he concluded that the creatures were alive. Years later scientists
called these micro-organisms 'bacteria'.

All foods contain bacteria, some of which can be harmful to us and some of
which can be good for us. The harmful bacteria need to be killed or reduced before
we eat the food or we might get food poisoning which could be fatal. This is why
most packaged foods today contain a label that tells us the sell-by date and the
use-by date. These dates are put there to protect us by making sure the food is still
fresh when it is eaten.

Milk and many canned foods are heated to a very high temperature before being
sold. This kills the bacteria. If this wasn't done, people could become very ill. Another
way to keep food safe is to dry it. Bacteria cannot live without water so dried foods
are safe to eat, but if moisture is added then the bacteria begin to grow again.

When food is put into a fridge or freezer, the bacteria do not die but their growth
rapidly slows down. Once the food is taken out of the cold and gets warm again, the
bacteria grow quickly and the food could become harmful. This is why thawed foods
should be cooked and eaten straight away. Bacteria can also be killed by removing
the air inside a package. This is why vacuum-packed foods can last for a very long
time. But once the seal is broken and air gets in the bacteria grow again.

◆ The text contains some examples of deduction, speculation and
   supposition. Read through the text again and do the following.

   1.   <u>Underline</u> examples of deduction in RED.

   2.   <u>Underline</u> examples of speculation in BLUE.

   3.   <u>Underline</u> examples of supposition in GREEN.

◆ Use the information in the text to complete the following.

_____ foods are heated to a high temperature, bacteria are killed, _____
if the foods are exposed to the air _____ bacteria can get in and
begin to grow. _____ moisture is added to dried foods
_____bacteria can begin to multiply. Vacuum-packed foods are
protected from bacteria _____ the seal is broken and air gets in.

◆ Share your ideas with someone else in your group. Do they agree with
   your choices?

Dissolving

◆ Literacy objectives

◆ To review the features of recounted texts: introduction to orientate the reader, chronological sequence, degree of formality adopted and use of connectives.
◆ To use the styles and conventions of journalism to report on an imagined event.

◆ Science objectives

◆ To understand that some solids can dissolve in water.
◆ To know that when solids dissolve a clear solution is formed.

◆ Resources

◆ Some newspaper articles.

◆ Starting point: Whole class

◆ Tell the children that they are going to read two different pieces of text about a murder! Explain that it is not a true event but one that has been made up. Tell them that each of the two passages has been written in a very different way from the other and that their task is to tell you all the differences they notice.
◆ Explain that they are then going to write a newspaper article about the murder, using the information from the shared texts.
◆ Share some of the newspaper articles to remind the children how newspaper articles are written and to revise the features of journalistic style – how the report should be balanced and ethical, how to engage the interest of the reader, what facts should be included and so on.

◆ Using the photocopiable text

◆ Enlarge the text on page 42 on a photocopier or arrange for each child to have a copy. Share the text.
◆ What differences do the children notice about the ways the texts are written? Discuss the use of impersonal language and the third person in the policeman's report. Point out the use of the passive voice, for example 'It has been decided...'
◆ Discuss the use of the first person in Dr Spot's report and how the language is less formal. What would have to change if the first text was written in the first person?
◆ Talk about the similarities between the texts – an introduction to orientate the reader, chronological sequencing of events and the use of connectives such as 'on arrival', 'but', 'firstly' and 'next'. What are the differences between the connectives in each text?
◆ Compare the two texts with the newspaper articles shared earlier. What are the differences and similarities in the style and language used? How might a newspaper article about the murder begin? What would be the most important facts to include in such a report?
◆ Explain that their task now is to write this newspaper report.

◆ Group activities

Using the differentiated activity sheets

Activity sheet 1: This is aimed at children who need a lot of support in writing a newspaper article. They are required to choose appropriate words from the policeman's report to complete the sentences.

Activity sheet 2: This is aimed at children who are more confident in writing a newspaper article. They are given the beginning and ending as a model and are required to complete the rest themselves.

Activity sheet 3: This is aimed at more able children. It requires them to write the newspaper article without any support at all.

Dissolving

◆ Plenary session

◆ Share the responses to the activity sheets. Have the children included all the relevant facts? Is it ethical to include the suspects' names at this stage? Have they written the article in a journalistic style? How does this text differ from the original two?

◆ Follow-up ideas for literacy

◆ Using the second text, Dr Spot's report, consider instructional writing and how the imperative form is used for this purpose. Ask the children to write the second text as a set of instructions.

◆ Ask the children to imagine they are Miss Pringle. How would this incident affect her? What might she write in her personal diary that night? Ask the children to write her diary.

◆ Ask the children to make up an epitaph for the well-respected Mr Coburg. What kind of man was he? What did others think of him? Share examples of epitaphs. Share suitable poems such as 'Requiem' by Robert Louis Stevenson.

◆ Ask the children to prepare a fictional CV for Miss Pringle in her search for a new job.

◆ Write a class newspaper using ICT.

◆ Dramatise the finding of the body, alerting the police and the policemen's responses.

◆ Follow-up ideas for science

◆ Test some different household liquids using universal indicator paper to find out how acidic they are.

◆ Ask the children to investigate a collection of solids to see which ones dissolve.

◆ Challenge the children to identify five white powders (plain flour, salt, baking powder, liver salts, cream of tartar). Mark the powders A–E. Provide hand lenses, universal indicator paper and vinegar (acetic acid). Give the children the information (see right) and explain that a similar murder has taken place but this time five powders have been found. Ask them to identify each powder.

Name	Dissolves?	Crystals?	Colour change	Vinegar response
liver salts	yes	yes	orange	bubbles
baking p.	no	no	blue/green	bubbles
tartar	no	no	yellow	no bubbles
flour	no	no	green	no bubbles
salt	yes	yes	green	no bubbles

Murder inquiry

Report from the scene of the crime by P.C. Alan Jones

The body of Mr James Coburg, investigative chemist, of 1 The Walk, Newville, was found by his secretary, Miss Pringle, at 1.30 pm on Friday March 30th, on her return from her morning off.

On arrival at the scene of the crime, it was difficult to ascertain the cause of death as the body was unmarked. However, two small plastic bags containing white powders were found on Mr Coburg's desk by P.C. Wood. It has been decided by Chief Constable Markham that these powders should be sent to the forensic laboratory for analysis. This may provide vital clues in the hunt for the murderer.

It has been discovered from Mr Coburg's diary that he had three appointments on Friday 30th March but there were no times written next to the appointments. The three people who had an appointment were: Mr Jones who was bringing with him a new formula for talcum powder, Mr Smith who was known to carry liver salts for his indigestion and Mrs Fugetti who was going to introduce Mr Coburg to her new pasta flour.

Once the identity of each powder has been ascertained by Dr Spot at the laboratory, it will be possible to determine which of the suspects visited Mr Coburg that morning.

Report of the investigation into the identity of two white powders

Firstly, on receiving the powders, I examined them with a hand lens and noted down whether they were powders or crystals.

Next, I added a small amount of acetic acid to each powder and watched to see if it bubbled.

Thirdly, I mixed each powder with water to see if it would dissolve.

Finally, I tested each solution with universal indicator paper to find out whether the solution was acid or alkali.

Putting the results together, I have discovered that the two white substances are talcum powder and liver salts.

Photocopiable
©Hopscotch Educational Publishing

✦ Newspaper report ✦

✦ Use P.C. Alan Jones' report to complete this
newspaper article about the murder of Mr Coburg.

Saturday
31st March 2001

The Daily Reporter

50p

MURDER SHOCKS LOCAL RESIDENTS

Local _____ were
shocked to find out that Mr James
_____, an investigative
chemist, was _____
yesterday.

Miss _____, who worked
for Mr Coburg, found the body at
1.30 pm after she returned to work
after having the _____ off.

Miss Pringle was very upset and
couldn't understand why _____
would want to kill Mr Coburg.

P.C. _____ told our
reporters that it was difficult to say
how Mr Coburg had died because
the body was _____.
He also said that three people were
due to _____ Mr Coburg
yesterday morning. The names of
these _____ have not yet
been released.

There were two plastic bags
containing white _____

found at the scene.

Chief Constable _____
is sending these powders to the
forensic laboratory for _____.

Anyone who thinks they may
have seen anything unusual outside
the building at 1 The Walk,
Newville, should _____
P.C. Alan Jones at the police station
immediately.

A police incident room has been
set up at the location.

◆ Newspaper report ◆

◆ Use P.C. Alan Jones' report to complete this newspaper article about the murder of Mr Coburg. Make sure you include ALL the important facts about the murder.

Saturday
31st March 2001

The Daily Reporter

50p

MURDER SHOCKS LOCAL RESIDENTS

Local residents were shocked to find out that Mr James Coburg, an investigative chemist, was murdered yesterday.

Miss Pringle, who worked for Mr Coburg, found

Anyone who thinks they may have seen anything unusual outside the building at 1 The Walk, Newville, should contact P.C. Alan Jones at the police station immediately.

A police incident room has been set up at the location.

Photocopiable
©Hopscotch Educational Publishing

✦ Newspaper report ✦

✦ Use P.C. Alan Jones' report to write a
newspaper article about the murder of
Mr Coburg. Make sure you include ALL
the important facts about the murder.

Saturday
31st March 2001

The Daily Reporter

50p

MURDER SHOCKS LOCAL RESIDENTS

Changes

◆ Literacy objectives

◆ To appraise a text quickly and effectively; to retrieve information from it; to find information quickly and evaluate its usefulness.
◆ To secure the skills of skimming and scanning and efficient reading so that research is fast and effective.

◆ Science objectives

◆ To understand that mixing materials can cause them to change.
◆ To know that insoluble materials can be separated by filtering, and solids that have dissolved can be recovered by evaporating the liquid from the solution.
◆ To understand that, when materials are burned, new materials are formed.
◆ To understand that the changes that occur when most materials are burned are not reversible.

◆ Resources

◆ A page from an information book (enough copies for the children to share or an OHP copy).

◆ Starting point: Whole class

◆ Tell the children that they are going to practise skimming and scanning techniques to learn how to find information quickly. Revise the meaning of the terms, that is: 'scanning' is to look over a text quickly, trying to locate information by finding key words and 'skimming' is finding the main ideas of a passage to provide an overview.
◆ Use the page from the information book to practise the skills. Show them how to read the first line of a paragraph or the words in bold on a page in order to obtain an idea of what the paragraph might be about. Tell them that in order to locate information quickly they need to omit any text they think is unlikely to contain the information they are looking for.

◆ Ask them to find the answer to a particular question. Show them how to scan the page, looking for key words, until they find the paragraph they think has the answer. Repeat this until the children understand the techniques.

◆ Using the photocopiable text

◆ Photocopy page 48, enough for each child or pair, and cut the pages into the two separate texts.
◆ Tell the children that they are going to help solve a problem. Explain that there has been a murder. The police have been investigating it and some of the evidence to be put forward in court is in the form of white powders. Dr Spot at the forensic laboratory has completed his tests on the powders to find out what they are but unfortunately his cleaning lady, Mrs Mopp, put water on to the dishes of powders, thinking they were finished with and needed a good soaking!
◆ Tell the children it is their task to scan the text you are going to give them to quickly find the answers to the following questions.
  1. How is a soluble substance removed from water?
  2. How is an insoluble substance removed from water?
◆ Before giving them the text (text 'A'), ask them to tell you what key words they think they will need to look for.
◆ Give or show the text, giving them sufficient time to scan it, but not long enough to read the complete text. Ask them which paragraphs they think they need to read in detail to find the answers. How do they know this?
◆ Explain that they will be doing a similar task using an activity sheet. (Children doing Activity sheets 2 and 3 should use text 'B' on page 48.)

Changes

 **Group activities**

Using the differentiated activity sheets

Activity sheet 1: This is aimed at children who need more support. Text 'B' has been simplified for these children. They are required to find the answers to three simple questions.

Activity sheet 2: This is aimed at children who are more confident in skimming and scanning. They are required to find the answers to six questions.

Activity sheet 3: This is aimed at more able children. It requires them to provide more detailed responses to more challenging questions.

Plenary session

✦ How many 'candle' words did they find? What strategies did they use to scan? Did they look for a word beginning with 'c' or a word ending in 'le'? How did they find the answers to the questions? Did they look for key words? When would skimming be useful in doing school work or when reading?

Follow-up ideas for literacy

✦ Make a list of the children's ideas of their strategies for skimming and scanning. Display the list so the children can refer to it when using skimming and scanning on other occasions.
✦ Give the children two short extracts on the same topic but from different sources. Ask them to evaluate the texts for their usefulness against a number of different criteria, for example: the most useful to draw a table or graph from, the most entertaining, the most informative, the one that describes technical words well and so on.
✦ Find more information about candles using CD-Roms, the Internet and encyclopaedias. What are their uses? How are they made?
✦ Reinforce skimming and scanning by using the same page from a newspaper or dictionary. Hunt for key words and words that rhyme or have a particular spelling pattern.

Follow-up ideas for science

✦ Carry out an experiment to separate sand, salt and rice. Mix the sand, salt and rice together. Provide the children with sieves, filter paper, funnels and beakers.
Ask them to plan how they are going to separate the three components of the mixture so that they can be used separately.
Remind the children to use the information in text 'A' to help them.
✦ Discuss what effect the temperature of the water might have on the amount of substance that will dissolve. Investigate, using a substance such as salt.

✦ Investigate the effect the volume of water may have on the amount of salt that will dissolve before the solution becomes saturated.
✦ Ask the children to write a list of things they think will change irreversibly after heating (such as raw egg or cake mixture) and a list of those things they think can be reversed (such as chocolate or water). Investigate the things on the lists.
✦ Carry out the candle experiment as in text 'B'. Make sure you stand the candle in a tray of sand. Observe any school/LEA safety guidelines.

Changes

A

Report from Dr Spot

On arriving at my laboratory on Saturday morning I was dismayed to find that Mrs Mopp, our new cleaning lady, had been rather too efficient and put water on to the remains of the white powders in the dishes, believing them to be finished with and needing cleaning up. Of course the powders were required in the court as evidence for the prosecution and there would be trouble if I couldn't produce them.

One of the powders was insoluble and the other one was soluble so I set about separating the insoluble powder from the water first.

When an insoluble substance is mixed with water, the best way to separate it is to use a filter paper, folded into a funnel. The insoluble substance and the water are poured into the funnel and the insoluble substance remains in the filter whilst the water goes through the filter paper into the dish.

If the substance is soluble, then the way to remove it from the water is different. The soluble substance has dissolved in the water and cannot be filtered out because the particles are too small to remain in the filter paper. Therefore you have to heat the solution gently and the water evaporates. As the water evaporates the soluble substance solidifies and remains in the dish.

Luckily for me, I had time to perform both of the separating techniques before the powders were required in court and no-one knows that the problem ever existed.

B

Candles

A candle is made from wax and has a strong wick down the centre. When it is lit, both the wax and the wick burn. Some people find this hard to believe as they think that the wax melts and only the wick burns. An experiment can be done to prove otherwise.

Take a candle and weigh it. Then light the candle and watch it burn. The flame has a hot centre where the wick is burning. The heat from the burning wax and wick melts the surrounding candle.

As you watch the candle burning you will notice that there is smoke rising from above the flame. If a piece of paper is carefully held above the flame, black soot will collect on the paper.

After the candle has been burning for a while, blow out the flame and weigh the candle again (including any wax that has fallen off). The candle will weigh less than it originally did because some of the wax has burned away.

Candles need oxygen to burn. Again this can be proved with a simple experiment.

Put a jam jar over the lighted candle and after a short time the candle will go out. This is because the oxygen has been used up.

Photocopiable

©Hopscotch Educational Publishing

✦ Candles ✦

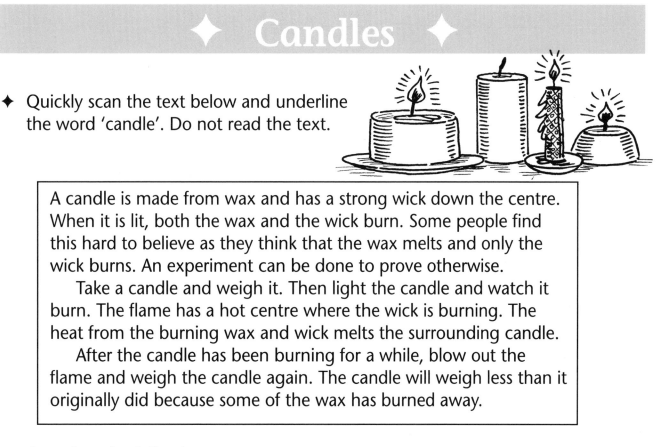

✦ Quickly scan the text below and underline the word 'candle'. Do not read the text.

> A candle is made from wax and has a strong wick down the centre. When it is lit, both the wax and the wick burn. Some people find this hard to believe as they think that the wax melts and only the wick burns. An experiment can be done to prove otherwise.
>
> Take a candle and weigh it. Then light the candle and watch it burn. The flame has a hot centre where the wick is burning. The heat from the burning wax and wick melts the surrounding candle.
>
> After the candle has been burning for a while, blow out the flame and weigh the candle again. The candle will weigh less than it originally did because some of the wax has burned away.

✦ Complete the following.

I found the word 'candle' ☐ times in the passage.

✦ From your quick scan of the text, what do you think the passage is about?

_____

✦ Answer these questions by skimming and scanning.

1. What are candles made from?_____

2. What parts of the candle burn when it is lit?_____

3. What causes the candle to melt?_____

✦ Now read the text all the way through. Briefly explain what the experiment proves.

◆ Candles ◆

◆ You will need a copy of text 'B' on candles. Quickly scan the text and underline the word 'candle' or 'candles'. Do not READ the passage.

◆ How many words did you find? ☐

◆ Now scan the text and circle the words 'burn' or 'burning'.

   How many did you find? ☐

◆ Skim and scan the text to find the answers to the following questions:

   1. What is a candle made from?_____

   2. What parts of a candle burn when it is lit?_____

   3. What causes the candle to melt?_____

   4. What rises above the flame when the candle is burning?_____

   5. If paper is held above the flame what will collect on it?_____

   6. Do candles need oxygen to burn?_____

◆ Now read through the whole text. Briefly explain what the experiment is and what it proves.

Photocopiable
©Hopscotch Educational Publishing

◆ Candles ◆

◆ You will need a copy of text 'B' on candles. Quickly scan the text and underline the word 'candle' or 'candles'. Do not READ the passage.

◆ How many words did you find? ☐

◆ Now scan the text and circle the words 'burn' or 'burning'.

How many did you find? ☐

◆ Skim and scan the text to find the answers to the following questions.

1. What is a candle made from?_____

2. What parts of a candle burn when it is lit?_____

3. Only some of the wax burns. What happens to the rest of the wax?

_____

4. Why do you need to weigh the candle at the beginning of the experiment?

_____

5. What does the wax give out as it burns?_____

6. How can you prove that oxygen is needed when a candle burns?

_____

◆ Now read through the whole text. Briefly explain what the experiment is and what it proves. Say whether you think the test is fair.

Interdependence & adaptation

◆ Literacy objectives

◆ To identify the features of balanced written arguments which, for example, summarise different sides of an argument, clarify the strengths and weaknesses of different positions and signal personal opinion clearly.

◆ To write a balanced report on a controversial issue, summarising fairly the competing views and analysing the strengths and weaknesses of different positions.

◆ Science objectives

◆ To understand that living things and the environment need protection.

◆ Resources

◆ Pictures of equatorial rainforests.

◆ Starting point: Whole class

◆ Think of an issue on which the children in your class are likely to have a strong opinion, for example compulsory homework.

◆ Tell the children that they are going to consider an important issue and give their opinions on it. Discuss your chosen issue and write up two lists of reasons for and against.

◆ Now explain what a balanced argument is and how difficult it can be to write about an issue without being biased. Explain that a balanced argument must put forward a summary of both sides of the argument, clarifying the strengths and weaknesses of different positions. It can also contain personal opinion but must still present points of view/facts from both sides. Discuss how difficult it can be to write objectively about something you have strong opinions about. Talk about how important it is to be aware of the standpoint of the writer when reading a non-fiction text.

◆ Model how to write a balanced argument from the class list of for and against.

◆ Using the photocopiable text

◆ Photocopy page 54, enough for each child or pair. Explain that they are going to read about another important issue. Share the texts and the pictures of the rainforests.

◆ Ask for comments on the differences between the two texts. Consider who the writer of each text might be from the tone and vocabulary used. What points does each writer make?

◆ Consider which phrases suggest bias on the part of the writer. Underline them.

◆ How useful might each text be if given as the only source of information to write a balanced report on the rainforests?

◆ Tell the children that they are going to consider this issue in more detail and will be writing their own report about it.

◆ Group activities

Using the differentiated activity sheets

Activity sheet 1: This is aimed at children who need more support. They are required to complete a passage using words from information provided.

Activity sheet 2: This is aimed at children who are able to use provided information to write their own balanced report.

Activity sheet 3: This is aimed at more able children. It requires them to use texts 1 and 2, underline the things they think are important in the argument about protecting the rainforests and then write their own balanced report.

Interdependence & adaptation

✦ *Plenary session*

✦ Share the responses to the activity sheets. Do they consider their reports to be balanced and fair? How difficult is it to present both sides of an argument? What things did the children in Groups 2 and 3 choose to write about? Do others agree that these are the most important points?

◆ *Follow-up ideas for literacy*

✦ Make a class collection of sentence connectives or phrases which are useful in replying to an argument or stating the other side of a case, for example 'on the other hand', 'therefore', 'however', 'consequently'.

✦ Provide opportunities for the children to write and speak on issues of interest to them, for example, creating a new set of playground rules, identifying ways to deal with unruly behaviour at playtimes.

✦ Write letters for a real purpose which can be sent to a local council, giving personal opinions about local issues, such as the need for a pedestrian crossing near school.

✦ Ask the children to find more information about the rainforests. Make a class book of the things they find out.

✦ Share stories about rainforest conservation, such as *Ronnie the Red-Eyed Tree Frog* by Martin and Tanis Jordan or *Where the Forest Meets the Sea* by Jeannie Baker. Encourage the children to write their own story.

◆ *Follow-up ideas for science*

✦ Investigate plant transpiration by placing plastic bags around the leaves of plants. Discuss what happens and why.

✦ Experiment with placing plants in various amounts of light to find out if there are any adverse effects.

✦ Study the plants and animals in a local habitat. Look at the ways they adapt to their environment. Find out how the plants and animals of the rainforest are adapted to their environment. Compare the plants and animals in the two habitats.

✦ Discuss the effect of soil erosion after land has been cleared of plants. Carry out an experiment to find out how plants prevent soil erosion.

You will need some soil, baking trays, cress seeds, watering-cans, bricks or other supports.

1. Fill the trays with soil and plant a lot of cress seeds in one tray, fewer in another and none in the third.

2. Water and wait until the cress has grown.

3. Stand the trays on a brick or other suitable support to make them slope. Pour water from a watering-can on the three trays and note what happens. Can the children think of a way to measure the changes they are observing?

The rainforests

Text 1

More than half the animal and plant species in the world live in the tropical rainforest ecosystems. They are often specialised, adapted to their habitat and quite unable to survive elsewhere. The world's rainforests are also home to an estimated two hundred million people. There are twenty thousand members of the Yanomami tribe living in the Amazon rainforest of Brazil alone. These people depend on the forest, finding nearly everything they need from the plants and animals living there.

Rainforests are sometimes called the lungs of the planet. Such enormous areas of trees take in carbon dioxide and give out oxygen and water on a huge scale. They make such a difference that they can affect the climate of the whole world! Plants found only in the rainforests provide vital medicines, which can be used to fight cancer and other serious illnesses.

We should not take risks with such a precious resource and yet we do! An area the size of a football pitch is destroyed not every **day** but every **second**! Since 1945, over half of the world's rainforests have been destroyed. For these it is too late, because once a rainforest is destroyed it cannot grow again, but we could try to save the rest of the forests if the governments were persuaded to work together to protect these seemingly huge but very fragile ecosystems.

Text 2

In Brazil, there are a million square miles of rainforest, surely enough to spare some for use by people who need to make a living. The forests contain some of the best and most valuable hardwoods in the world. The markets of Europe and North America pay high prices for the teak, ebony and mahogany wood for furniture making. Why shouldn't poorer countries be able to sell their wood so they can support and educate their own people?

Once the trees have been removed, local people can use the land for farming. There are even government grants in some areas to encourage people to move into the forests and farm. Why then should there be criticism of those who take up this offer?

People say that cattle ranching is destroying the forests of South America but we have to consider what the ranchers are giving in return. The meat they produce is sold at a good profit to big companies in North America. At least some of the revenue from this sale is returned to South America.

There are natural resources like oil and metals under the ground beneath the forests too. Why shouldn't countries with rainforests be able to use them to benefit their own people when other countries are allowed to exploit *their* natural resources?

✦ The rainforests ✦

✦ Read these comments made by different
Brazilian people about the rainforests.

The forests have been my home and that of my ancestors for hundreds of years. We can get all that we need from the forest.

Cutting down trees is an excellent idea because it gives my family somewhere to farm.

Poor countries must be allowed to cut down and sell rainforest woods to make money.

The forest is home to thousands of plants and animals. Many of them cannot live anywhere else. The forests should not be destroyed.

tribesman   cattle rancher   government official   scientist

✦ Use the comments above to complete this report about the rainforests.

Scientists tell us that the rainforest is home to thousands of _____
and _____. Many of these cannot live _____else. This is a
very important reason why they should not be _____. Many
people live in the forests too. They can get all that they _____ from
the forests. Cattle ranchers make a lot of money by cutting down the
_____ and making _____. The governments of poorer
countries think they should be allowed to cut down and sell _____ to
make money.

✦ Now add a final comment of your own to the passage above. What do YOU
think?

◆ The rainforests ◆

◆ Read the sentences below about the rainforests.

1. Cutting down the trees in the rainforests is an excellent idea because it enables people to make money by farming the land.

2. The Yanomami people are happy to live in the forests as they have done for centuries. They can get all they need from the forest.

3. There are thousands of species of plants and animals that live in the rainforests. Many of them cannot live anywhere else so it is important that the forests are not destroyed.

4. Poorer countries should be allowed to make money from the rainforests in any way they can. After all, other countries are allowed to sell their resources.

5. The rainforests are special. Once cut down, they cannot regrow. We should save them now before it is too late.

6. Governments should be encouraging people to make money in other ways, without destroying the forests.

◆ Use the information in these sentences to write your own report about the rainforests. Make sure your report is balanced and includes points of view from both sides of the argument.

Photocopiable
©Hopscotch Educational Publishing

✦ The rainforests ✦

✦ You will need a copy of texts 1 and 2 about the rainforests. You are going to write a balanced report about the rainforests. Read the two passages and underline the parts you think are important enough to be included in your report.

✦ Now use these underlined sections to help you write the report. Decide on the order you will write the points you chose. Think carefully about how you will begin your report to make sure it attracts the attention of the reader. Make sure your report is balanced and contains points of view from both sides of the argument.

✦ Write your report here.

✦ Compare your report with others in your group. Have you chosen the same information to use? Are the reports fair and balanced?

Forces

 **Literacy objectives**

+ To distinguish between biography and autobiography.
+ To develop the skills of biographical writing in role through writing an obituary.

Science objectives

+ To understand that objects are pulled downwards because of the gravitational attraction between them and the Earth.
+ To understand the part that science has played in the development of many useful things.

Resources

+ Samples of obituaries.

Starting point: Whole class

+ Tell the children that they will be doing some work on obituaries. Explain the meaning of the word. Discuss the reasons for composing an obituary. What kind of information might be included? What kinds of people are usually written about?
+ Share some sample obituaries. Consider the styles in which they are written and the reasons for adopting the style. Who do they think may have written them? Discuss the fact that they are usually written by a member of the family, a close friend or perhaps a journalist who has carried out research on the person.
+ Talk about how the obituary is a tribute to the person's life and how particular important facts are selected from the life story of the person involved. Would only good things be mentioned? Why?/Why not?
+ You may want to model how to write an obituary using a list of facts about a real or imaginary person.

Using the photocopiable text

+ Photocopy page 60, enough for each child or pair to have their own copy. Explain that they are now going to read another piece of writing about a famous person.
+ Share the text. Is this an obituary? Why not? What kind of writing is it?
+ Discuss the genre of autobiography and how it differs from a biography. Compare the effect on the reader of the choice between first and third person. Discuss the differences between fact, fiction and opinion. Which type of writing might contain more fiction and/or opinion? Why? Distinguish between implicit and explicit points of view and how these can differ – what can we infer about the personality of Isaac Newton from reading the text? What do the children think is factual and what is anecdotal?
+ Explain that you now want them to use the information about Isaac Newton to write an obituary.

Group activities

Using the differentiated activity sheets

Activity sheet 1: This is aimed at children who need support in finding the main facts in a text and in writing an obituary. They are required to use a list of facts to complete an obituary.

Activity sheet 2: This is aimed at children who are able to use a list of provided facts to write an obituary.

Activity sheet 3: This is aimed at more able children. It requires them to use the autobiography of Isaac Newton, shared in class, and decide for themselves what the main facts should be in order to write an obituary of the man.

Forces

©Hopscotch Educational Publishing

◆ *Plenary session*

✦ Share the responses to the activity sheets. Are they happy with their finished work or could it be improved in some way? Ask the children to comment constructively on the style and tone of some of the obituaries. Discuss the reasons for any differences noted. Compare the facts selected by those children using Activity sheet 3 amongst others in their group and that of sheets 1 and 2.

◆ *Follow-up ideas for literacy*

✦ Share other examples of autobiographies and biographies. Ask the children to write a biography based on their own research of another famous scientist or write a description of the person from a different viewpoint such as a school report or newspaper article.

✦ Challenge the children to write an obituary of Isaac Newton as if written by one of his rivals. How might the tone and content change?

✦ Ask the children to write a letter as though from Newton, giving his opinions and details of his life at his grandmother's house before he went to grammar school. Challenge them to convey his feelings as inferred in the text.

✦ Share some CVs. Look at the way they are presented and the type of language used. Ask the children to write the CV of an invented person or one for themselves.

✦ Research the life of Newton more fully. What other theories did he develop? What is he best known for?

◆ *Follow-up ideas for science*

✦ Discuss the children's own knowledge about gravity. Pose the question: 'Does the weight of an object alter the time it takes for it to hit the ground from a certain height?' Ask the children to write a hypothesis which can be tested.

✦ Investigate air resistance by comparing the rates of fall of a sheet of paper and the same sheet of paper screwed up into a ball. Which one falls faster? Why?

✦ Ask the children to use secondary sources to find more information about the forces of gravity.

✦ Ask the children to investigate parachutes and how they fall. Make the initial parachute with a piece of paper and four pieces of cotton thread, one tied to each corner. Attach a plastic weight to the thread. Throw the parachute up into the air and watch how it descends. Ask the children to experiment with different lengths of string, different materials for the canopy, different sized canopies and different shaped canopies. Ask them to determine which one offers the most resistance and offers the smoothest fall. Can they suggest why?

Isaac Newton

I was born in 1642 and I remember when I was very young, perhaps only three, being told by my mother that I had to go and live with my grandmother in Lincolnshire. My father had died; I can hardly remember him, and my mother was remarrying.

I recall that I stayed indoors a lot at my grandmother's. Not many children came to play. Mostly I made models or read books. As I grew, I studied mathematics, which was always my favourite subject, at the grammar school in Grantham.

I worked hard at Cambridge University and wanted to stay and carry on my research, but the very year I got my degree, they closed the university because of an outbreak of plague there. Still, I made the best of it. I went to stay with my mother on her farm, not to become a farmer, you understand, but to make the most of the peace and quiet to think and try out my mathematical theories. I do believe, looking back, that I was better at mathematics then than at any other time in my life, even when I was Professor of Mathematics at Cambridge. I was the youngest ever. I was only 26 when I was appointed.

*Even at Cambridge, in later years, I spent a lot of my time working alone. You see, mine wasn't the kind of work you could do with others – not really. Besides, some of the ideas I was working on were so new that sometimes there was great opposition to them when I finally persuaded myself to publish them. I hated all that – the letters to the newspapers, protests at my ideas, people making a mockery of my work, even colleagues writing to say that I had stolen **their** ideas! How dare they! I am afraid they would steal **my** ideas given the opportunity.*

I suppose I will be best remembered for my contribution to mathematics and of course, to physics. It was I who developed theories about forces and motions that other learned men are saying will still be taught four hundred years from now! I studied gravity and tried to explain how all the planets stay in orbit. And I remember well the criticisms I got because my diagrams of the solar system did not contain God and His angels! Still, I suppose all new theories upset someone. I just hope that in years to come my contribution will seem to have been useful. It is pleasant, near the end of my days here on Earth, to think that I, Isaac Newton, might have made a difference.

Photocopiable
©Hopscotch Educational Publishing

✦ Isaac Newton ✦

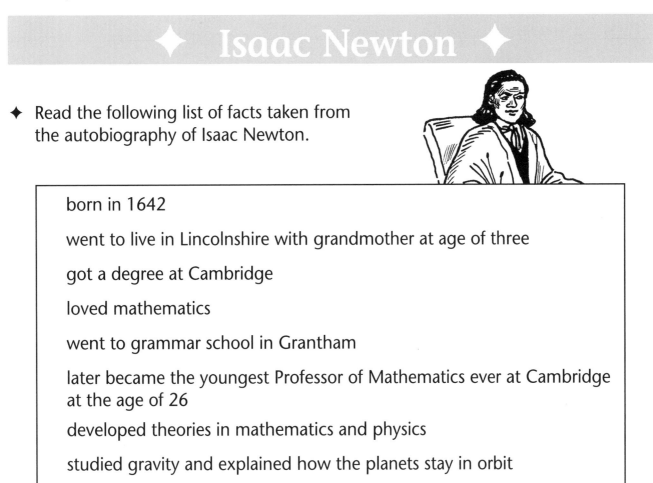

✦ Read the following list of facts taken from the autobiography of Isaac Newton.

born in 1642

went to live in Lincolnshire with grandmother at age of three

got a degree at Cambridge

loved mathematics

went to grammar school in Grantham

later became the youngest Professor of Mathematics ever at Cambridge at the age of 26

developed theories in mathematics and physics

studied gravity and explained how the planets stay in orbit

✦ Use the list to complete this obituary of Newton.

The death was announced yesterday of Mr Isaac Newton of Grantham, Lincolnshire. Mr Newton was born in _____ and went to live with his _____ at the age of three on his father's death. He always had a great love of _____ and enjoyed studying it at the grammar school in _____. Later on, Mr Newton was to study at the University of _____ where he later became the youngest ever Professor of _____ at the age of _____. Mr Newton was well known for his incredible theories in mathematics and _____. He made a special study of _____ and tried to explain how the planets stay in _____. Not everyone agreed with his theories but Mr Isaac Newton will be sorely missed because he was an inspiration to all young mathematicians.

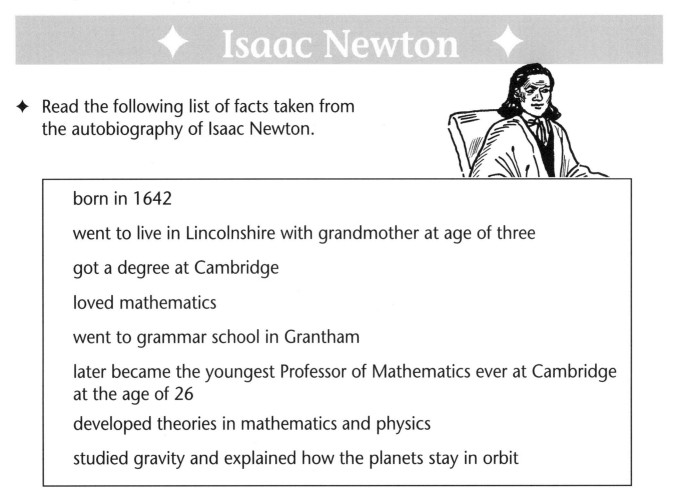

Isaac Newton

✦ Read the following list of facts taken from
the autobiography of Isaac Newton.

born in 1642

went to live in Lincolnshire with grandmother at age of three

got a degree at Cambridge

loved mathematics

went to grammar school in Grantham

later became the youngest Professor of Mathematics ever at Cambridge
at the age of 26

developed theories in mathematics and physics

studied gravity and explained how the planets stay in orbit

✦ Now use the list to complete this obituary of Isaac Newton.

*The death was announced yesterday of Mr Isaac Newton of Grantham, Lincolnshire.
Mr Newton was*

Photocopiable
©Hopscotch Educational Publishing

✦ Isaac Newton ✦

✦ You will need the text containing the autobiography of Isaac Newton.

Read the text through again and underline all the important things you think should go in an obituary of him.

✦ Make a list of these things here.

✦ Now use the list to complete this obituary of Isaac Newton.

The death was announced yesterday of Mr Isaac Newton of Grantham, Lincolnshire. Mr Newton was